ACHIEVE

Year **6**

Reading

SATs Practice Papers

Laura Collinson & Shareen Mayers

RISING STARS

The Publishers would like to thank the following for permission to reproduce copyright material.

Photo credits
Photos from iStock: p12 Buckingham Palace © Keattikorn; p22 Pharos lighthouse © BORTEL Pavel – Pavelmidi; p38 ice cyrstals © Rumo Photos from Shutterstock: p13 Windsor Castle © sloukam; p24 Longstone lighthouse © Attila JANDI; p39 salt crystals © Ranglen; p40 diamond ring © Serggod; p49 Marianne North © rook76; p50 palki © Jorg Hackemann

Text extracts
pp6–7 'Theseus and the Minotaur' featured on http://myths.e2bn.org; pp12–13 'Do you Believe in Ghosts?' By Rick Barry, Reprinted with permission of Answers in Genesis (www.answersingenesis.org); 'Things that go BUMP in the night!' Adapted from 'Ghosts of the past: 5 haunted royal residences' by Wesley McDermott; pp19–20 'The lion and Albert' by Marriott Edgar, Reprinted with permission of Warner/Chappell Production Music; pp26–27 Adapted from *Lighthouses of England: The North East* by Nicholas Leach and Tony Denton (Foxglove Media, 2010); pp27–28 'Frequently Asked Questions' http://www.rondaarmitage.co.uk/frequently-asked-question © Ronda Armitage; pp33–34 Adapted from *The Hollow Land* by Jane Gardam © David Higham Associates; pp39–40 'The Lady of Shalott' by Alfred Lord Tennyson; pp44–46 468 words adapted from *Crystal & Gem* by R.F. Symes (Dorling Kindersley, 2000). Copyright© Dorling Kindersley Ltd London; pp51–52 Excerpt from 'Macavity: The Mystery Cat' from *Old Possum's Book of Cats* by T.S. Eliot. Copyright 1939 by T.S. Eliot. Copyright © Renewed 1967 by Esme Valerie Eliot. Reprinted with permission of Faber and Faber and Houghton Mifflin Harcourt Publishing Company. All rights reserved; pp56–58 Adapted from *Abundant Beauty* by Marianne North reprinted with permission from Greystone Books Ltd.

Every effort has been made to trace all copyright holders, but if any have been inadvertently overlooked, the Publishers will be pleased to make the necessary arrangements at the first opportunity.

Although every effort has been made to ensure that website addresses are correct at time of going to press, Rising Stars cannot be held responsible for the content of any website mentioned in this book. It is sometimes possible to find a relocated web page by typing in the address of the home page for a website in the URL window of your browser.

Hachette UK's policy is to use papers that are natural, renewable and recyclable products and made from wood grown in sustainable forests. The logging and manufacturing processes are expected to conform to the environmental regulations of the country of origin.

Orders: please contact Bookpoint Ltd, 130 Park Drive, Milton Park, Abingdon, Oxon OX14 4SE. Telephone: (44) 01235 400555. Email: primary@bookpoint.co.uk.

Lines are open from 9 a.m. to 5 p.m., Monday to Saturday, with a 24-hour message answering service. Visit our website at www.risingstars-uk.com for details of the full range of Rising Stars publications.

Online support and queries email: onlinesupport@risingstars-uk.com

ISBN: 978 1 51044 261 0

© Hodder & Stoughton Ltd. (for its Rising Stars imprint) 2019

This edition published in 2018 by Rising Stars, part of Hodder & Stoughton Ltd.

First published in 2015 by Rising Stars, part of Hodder & Stoughton Ltd.

Rising Stars is part of the Hodder Education Group

An Hachette UK Company

Carmelite House

50 Victoria Embankment

London EC4Y 0DZ

www.risingstars-uk.com

impression number 10 9 8 7 6 5 4

Year 2022 2021 2020 2019

Authors: Laura Collinson and Shareen Mayers

Series Editor: Helen Lewis

Accessibility Reviewer: Vivien Kilburn

Cover design: Burville-Riley Partnership

Illustrations by Dave Burroughs

Typeset in India

Printed in the UK

A catalogue record for this title is available from the British Library.

Contents

The answers can be found in a pull-out section in the middle of this book.

Introduction

About the Practice Tests for reading

The tests are intended for use during the spring and summer terms of Year 6 in preparation for the National Tests. They are written to cover the content domain of the *Key Stage 2 English reading test framework for the National Curriculum tests from 2016* (Standards & Testing Agency, 2015). The tests **as a whole** provide complete coverage of the content domain.

There are three tests in total and each test contains three texts, covering a balance of fiction, non-fiction and poetry. Test demand increases within each test, as in the National Test, so initial questions are generally easier than those towards the end of each test, allowing for the chronology to remain correct.

To reduce the amount of referring back and forth between answer sections and texts, we have located the questions after each text rather than at the end of the test. To minimise this further, you may choose to collate your photocopied pages into a texts booklet and an answer booklet.

How to use the Practice Tests

Preparation and timings

1 Help your child prepare for each paper by simulating test conditions.
2 Ensure your child is seated appropriately in front of the paper they are going to work on.
3 Your child will need pens or pencils, and erasers.
4 There are no time limits for the tests but normal practice is to allow a minute per mark for written tests. Help with reading may be given using the same rules as when providing a reader with the Key Stage 2 tests.

Supporting children during the tests

Before the test explain to your child that the test is an opportunity to show what they know, understand and can do. They should try to answer all the questions but should not worry if there are some they can't do.

Many children will be able to work independently in the tests, with minimal support. However, children should be encouraged to 'have a go' at a question, or to move on to a fresh question if they appear to be stuck. Return to difficult questions if you have enough time at the end.

It is important that children receive appropriate support, but are not unfairly advantaged or disadvantaged. Throughout the tests, therefore, you may read, explain or sign to a child any parts of the test that include instructions, for example by demonstrating how to fill in a table.

Marking the tests

Use the mark scheme and your own judgement to award marks. Do not award half marks. Note that a number of questions in each test may require children to do more than one thing for one mark. The mark scheme provides clear guidance in the allocation of marks to support consistent marking of the tests.

It is useful for your child to mark their own test questions from time to time. Your child can look at the test sheets and mark them as you read out the question and answer. You will need to check that your child is marking accurately. This approach also provides an opportunity to recap on any questions that your child found difficult to answer.

Keep track of your child's score using the table on the inside back cover of this book.

Test 1

The story of the Minotaur

King Minos of Crete was a powerful man, feared by the rulers of the lands around him. But his demands on Athens became too much for them to bear.

King Minos had a great palace built for himself. Inside this palace, Minos had built a giant maze, a labyrinth, and at the centre of the maze he kept a terrifying creature, the Minotaur. Now this was no ordinary animal; it was a monster, half man and half bull.

It was powerful and savage and it loved to eat the flesh of the humans who had been shut into the labyrinth by King Minos.

As for Athens, Minos demanded that every year the king send him seven young men and seven young women.

'Why do we send these young people to Crete every year?' Theseus asked his father, the King of Athens. 'And why is it that none of them ever return?'

'Because if we did not send them, Minos would wage war on us and it is a war that we would not win,' said King Aegeus. 'And they do not return because they do not go to Crete as slaves. They go as food for the Minotaur.'

'Father, this is terrible,' shouted Theseus, 'we cannot let this go on. We cannot sacrifice any more of our young citizens to this tyrant. When it is time to send the next tribute, I will go as one of them and I vow that it is the last time the Minotaur will be fed with the flesh of any of our people.'

'Then I wish you good luck, my son,' cried his father, 'I shall keep watch for you every day. If you are successful, take down these black sails and replace them with white ones. That way, I will know you are coming home safe to me.'

As the ship docked in Crete, King Minos himself came down to inspect the prisoners from Athens.

Theseus stepped forward. 'I will go first. I am Theseus, Prince of Athens, and I do not fear what is within the walls of your maze.'

Standing behind the king, listening, was his daughter, Ariadne. From the moment she set eyes on Theseus, Ariadne fell in love with him and decided that she would help him.

'Theseus, take this,' she whispered. She threw him a great ball of string and he tied one end of it to the entrance. He smiled at her, turned and began to make his way into the maze, the string playing out behind him as he went.

Turning a corner, with his hands held out in front of him feeling his way, Theseus suddenly touched what felt like a huge bony horn.

He was picked up between the Minotaur's horns and tossed high into the air. When he landed on the hard cold stone, he felt the animal's huge hooves come down on his chest.

But Theseus was no ordinary man. He was the son of the king, he was brave and he was stubborn.

He grabbed the animal's huge horns, and kept on twisting the great head from side to side. The creature's neck snapped, it gurgled its last breath and fell to the floor with an enormous thud.

As Theseus neared the entrance of the labyrinth, the darkness began to fade and he made out the figure of Ariadne, waiting for his return.

'You must take me back to Athens with you,' she cried. 'My father will kill me when he finds out that I have helped you.'

Quickly and quietly, they unfurled the great black sails of their ship and headed for home.

'I cannot believe how my life has changed,' said Ariadne, as they sailed across the calm seas towards Athens. 'To think that I am free of my cruel father and that I will soon be married to a great prince.'

'Married?' said Theseus. 'Oh, yes, that will be … er … wonderful.' But in truth, Theseus did not really find her attractive.

So, when their ship docked at an island on their way home to collect fresh water, Theseus sent Ariadne off to find bread and fruit. The moment she was gone, he set sail and left her on the island. Now, you might think that this was a bad way to reward someone who had helped him and had saved him from certain death.

The gods clearly thought the same thing, for they had a further horror in store for him, as a punishment for his ungrateful treatment of the young girl.

In his haste to get away, Theseus forgot to change his sails to white. King Aegeus, waiting on the headland, saw the ship approaching with its black sails flying in the wind. 'My son has failed and he is dead,' he cried. And in despair, he flung himself from the cliff into the raging waters below.

| Name: | Class: | Date: | Total marks: | /50 |

1 *Inside this palace, Minos had built a giant maze, a labyrinth, and at the centre of the maze he kept a* **terrifying** *creature.*

Which word is closest in meaning to *terrifying*?

Tick **one**.

mighty ☐

petrifying ☐

amazing ☐

powerful ☐

1 mark

2 The story explains that King Minos demanded that people from Athens be sent to him to feed the Minotaur.

What does this tell you about the character of King Minos?

Give **two** features of his character.

1. _____

2. _____

2 marks

3 *It was powerful and savage and it loved to eat the flesh of the humans who had been shut into the labyrinth by King Minos.*

What is this a description of?

_____

1 mark

/4

Total for this page

4 Look at what Theseus says to his father in the paragraph beginning: *'Father, this is terrible ...'*

What is the **main** reason for his decision to go to Crete?

_____

_____

1 mark

5 *'We cannot sacrifice any more of our young citizens to this* **tyrant**.*'*

Why was *tyrant* an appropriate word to describe King Minos?

Tick **one**.

He was unfriendly. ☐

He was serious. ☐

He was cruel. ☐

He was caring. ☐

1 mark

6 How does the final paragraph link back to the paragraph beginning: *'Then I wish you good luck, my son,'* cried his father?

_____

_____

_____

2 marks

/ 4

Total for this page

7 What did King Aegeus tell Theseus to do to signal Theseus's safe return?

1 mark

_____

8 Look at the paragraph beginning: *Standing behind the king ...*

Why did Ariadne insist that Theseus should take her back to Athens with him?

1 mark

_____

_____

9 Look at the paragraph beginning: *'You must take me back to Athens ...,'* to the end of the story.

Give **two** things that Ariadne did that show she did not agree with her father.

2 marks

1. _____

2. _____

10 What do you think Ariadne did when she found out Theseus had sailed away without her?

1 mark

_____

_____

/ 5

Total for this page

11 Look at the paragraph beginning: *The gods clearly thought the same thing …*

Find and **copy** the word which means that the gods were about to give Theseus a shock.

_____

12 How do you think Aegeus felt when he saw the sails were black?

Give **one** feeling, using evidence from the text to support your answer.

Feeling _____

Evidence _____

_____

_____

13 Number the following events 1–5 to show the order in which they happened.

The first one has been done for you.

At the centre of the maze was the Minotaur. ☐

Theseus is picked up by the Minotaur. ☐

King Minos builds a giant maze. 1

Aegeus presumes that Theseus has died. ☐

Theseus and Ariadne sail across the calm seas. ☐

Things that go BUMP in the night!

Contents
Do you believe in ghosts?
What is a ghost?
Ghosts at royal residences
Royal ghosts – at what cost?

Do you believe in ghosts?

Ghosts. What do you really think about them? Is it true that most of us love a good scary ghost story? Children and adults alike wonder about the existence of ghosts. Some reject the notion. Others insist that ghosts exist and tell of experiences – their own or friend-of-a-friend stories – as proof.

What is a ghost?

Although definitions vary, the most common one is that ghosts are spirits of dead people that linger on Earth. According to tradition, ghosts are invisible but can permit humans to see them.

Of course, either a thing exists or it doesn't. No amount of belief will cause ghosts to exist if they don't; nor could personal opinion cause ghosts not to exist if, in fact, they truly do exist.

Ghosts at royal residences

Where better to kick things off than the Queen's official workplace and London residence, Buckingham Palace.

It is said that the rear terrace of Buckingham Palace is haunted by the ghost of an enchained monk in a brown cowl. He is believed to be the spirit of a monk who died in a punishment cell from a time when a monastery stood on the site.

Another ghost that has been reported is that of Major John Gwynne, who served as King Edward VII's private secretary. After his divorce from his wife, the Major was shunned by upper society. Unable to cope with a life of shame, he died in his first floor office.

Windsor Castle is perhaps the most haunted of all the royal residences, with as many as 25 ghosts reported. The ghost of Elizabeth I has been seen by several members of the royal family, including Queen Elizabeth II and her sister Margaret. Often seen in the library, her footsteps can be heard on the bare floorboards, before her striking presence appears.

The ghost of George III has been witnessed, looking longingly out of the room beneath the library, where he was confined during his several periods of madness.

Henry VIII is said to haunt the deanery cloisters, often heard hobbling around, the sound of his ulcerated leg thudding on the floor as he walks.

One of the most notorious ghosts of Balmoral Castle is that of John Brown. Servant to Queen Victoria, they apparently fell in love; however, this remains a matter of conjecture. His ghost is often seen walking the corridors, usually wearing a kilt. Queen Elizabeth II has also reported the feeling of his presence throughout the castle.

Royal ghosts — at what cost?

Of course, ghostly experiences at royal residences are great news for conservationists, who often struggle to meet the rising costs of maintaining these rather grand buildings. Tourist tickets are a major contributor in developing the funds necessary to preserve the buildings and their contents. In return, tourists are treated to British history at first hand, and if they are really lucky, a ghostly sighting! However, the increase in tourist activity can have a potentially damaging effect on our living history. It has been said that many objects have been worn out and even stolen occasionally. Car parks have had to be created and the grounds maintained to accommodate vast numbers of vehicles. Littering, though not a major concern at the moment, has also contributed to an increase in maintenance costs. Despite the fact that tickets are arguably expensive, thousands of tourists still flock to the royal palaces every year.

14 Look at the section headed: *Do you believe in ghosts?*

What would be a suitable replacement for this sub-heading?

1 mark

Tick **one**.

Do children believe in ghosts?	☐
Do you think ghosts exist?	☐
Do adults believe ghosts exist?	☐
Are ghost stories real?	☐

15 Who wonders about the existence of ghosts?

Give **two** different examples.

1 mark

1. _____

2. _____

16 Look at the section headed: *Do you believe in ghosts?*

Find and **copy one** word that is closest in meaning to *a thought*.

1 mark

_____

/3

Total for this page

14

17 Look at the section headed: **What is a ghost?**

Can ghosts be seen by everyone?

Find and **copy one** line from the text that explains this.

_____

_____

1 mark

18 a) The main idea in the section headed **Ghosts at royal residences** is that Buckingham Palace is ...

1 mark

Tick **one**.

not haunted. ☐

the home of the Queen. ☐

haunted. ☐

the home of John Gwynne. ☐

b) Give **one** detail to support this idea.

_____

1 mark

19 Look at the paragraph beginning: *Windsor Castle is perhaps the most haunted ...*

Find and **copy one** word that is closest in meaning to *a person's home.*

_____

1 mark

/4

Total for this page 15

20 Who has been viewed by several members of the royal family?

_____

1 mark

21 *The ghost of George III has been witnessed, looking longingly out of the room beneath the library ...*

What does the word *longingly* tell you about how he felt?

_____

_____

1 mark

22 Look at the paragraph beginning: *One of the most notorious ghosts of Balmoral Castle ...*

Find and **copy one** word that suggests that the idea that Queen Victoria and John Brown fell in love may **not** be true.

_____

1 mark

23 Which ghost wears a kilt?

_____

1 mark

/4

Total for this page

24 Match each ghost to the place in which it has been sighted.

One has been done for you.

2 marks

Ghost	Place

George III		corridors
a monk		library
Henry VIII		rear terrace
John Brown		room beneath the library
Elizabeth I		cloisters

(George III connected to room beneath the library)

25 Look at the section headed: *Royal ghosts – at what cost?*

Explain **one** positive and **one** negative outcome, using evidence from the text to support your answer.

3 marks

Positive:

_____

_____

_____

Negative:

_____

_____

_____

26 Draw lines to match each section to its main content.

One has been done for you.

1 mark

Section   **Content**

| Contents | highlights the different ghosts that lived in palaces and castles |

| Do you believe in ghosts? | presents the differing viewpoints on having ghosts |

| What is a ghost? | introduces the debate about whether or not ghosts exist |

| Ghosts at royal residences | shows what is inside the book |

| Royal ghosts – at what cost? | gives information about the description of a ghost |

/ 1

Total for this page

The lion and Albert

There's a famous seaside place called Blackpool,
That's noted for fresh air and fun,
And Mr and Mrs Ramsbottom
Went there with young Albert, their son.

A grand little lad was their Albert,
All dressed in his best; quite a swell
'E'd a stick with an 'orse's 'ead 'andle,
The finest that Woolworth's could sell.

They didn't think much of the ocean:
The waves, they was fiddlin' and small
There was no wrecks and nobody drownded,
Fact, nothing to laugh at at all.

So, seeking for further amusement,
They paid and went into the zoo,
Where they'd lions and tigers and camels,
And old ale and sandwiches too.

There were one great big lion called Wallace;
His nose were all covered with scars –
He lay in a somnolent posture,
With the side of his face to the bars.

Now Albert had heard about lions,
How they were ferocious and wild –
To see Wallace lying so peaceful,
Well, it didn't seem right to the child.

So straightway the brave little feller,
Not showing a morsel of fear,
Took his stick with the 'orse's 'ead 'andle
And pushed it in Wallace's ear.

You could see that the lion didn't like it,
For giving a kind of a roll,
He pulled Albert inside the cage with 'im,
And swallowed the little lad 'ole.

Then Pa, who had seen the occurrence,
And didn't know what to do next,
Said, "Mother! Yon lion's 'et Albert",
And Mother said "Well, I am vexed!"

So Mr and Mrs Ramsbottom –
Quite rightly, when all's said and done –
Complained to the Animal Keeper,
That the lion had eaten their son.

The keeper was quite nice about it ;
He said "What a nasty mishap.
Are you sure that it's your boy he's eaten?"
Pa said "Am I sure? There's his cap!"

The manager had to be sent for.
He came and he said, "What's to do?"
Pa said, "Yon lion's 'et Albert,
And 'im in his Sunday clothes, too."

Then Mother said, "Right's right, young feller;
I think it's a shame and a sin,
For a lion to go and eat Albert,
And after we've paid to come in."

The manager wanted no trouble
He took out his purse right away,
Saying "How much to settle the matter?"
And Pa said "What do you usually pay?"

But Mother had turned a bit awkward
When she thought where her Albert had gone
She said "No! someone's got to be summonsed" –
So that were decided upon.

Round they went to the P'lice Station
In front of the Magistrate chap;
They told 'im what happened to Albert
And proved it by showing his cap.

The Magistrate gave his opinion
That no one was really to blame
And he said that he hoped the Ramsbottoms
Would have further sons to their name.

At that Mother got proper blazing.
"And thank you, sir, kindly," said she
"What waste all our lives raising children
To feed ruddy lions? Not me!"

27 Look at the first verse.

Find and **copy one** word that is closest in meaning to *well known*.

_____

1 mark

28 **Find** and **copy** a line from the poem that shows it is written in dialect.

_____

1 mark

29 Look at the third and fourth verses.

Write the main idea of these verses in **one** sentence.

_____

1 mark

30 What animals were at the zoo?

Give **two** different animals.

1. _____

2. _____

1 mark

/ 4

Total for this page

31 Why did Albert decide to provoke the lion?

_____

_____

1 mark

32 *So straightway the brave little feller*

Not showing a morsel of fear

Why has the word *morsel* been used to describe the boy's fear?

_____

_____

1 mark

33 What did Albert do to show that he was not afraid of the lion?

_____

_____

1 mark

/3

Total for this page

34 Look at the verses beginning: *Now Albert had heard about lions …* and: *So straightway the brave little feller …*

What do these verses tell you about Albert's character?

Explain **two** features of his character, using evidence from the text to support your answer.

1. _____

_____

_____

2. _____

_____

_____

35 Look at the verse beginning: *So the manager had to be sent for …*

and ending: *And 'im in his Sunday clothes, too."*

What does *Sunday clothes* mean?

_____

_____

36 Look at the verse beginning: *Then Mother said, "Right's right, young feller …*

How is Mother feeling?

Explain **one** feeling, using evidence from the text to support your answer.

Feeling _____

Evidence _____

_____

_____

2 marks

37 The poem suggests that …

Tick **one**.

life is great.	☐
family days out are fun.	☐
life is unpredictable.	☐
family is important.	☐

1 mark

/3

Total for this page

38 What is the purpose of this poem?

Tick **one**.

to entertain ☐

to scare ☐

to inform ☐

to tempt ☐

1 mark

39 Mother's opinion towards saving Albert changes by the end of the poem.

Explain this change.

_____

_____

1 mark

/2

Total for this page

Test 2

Lighthouse history

Why were lighthouses built?

Lighthouses were constructed to mark the major headlands and sandbanks. On a smaller scale, lights were also erected at the entrances to ports, harbours and rivers.

The first lights

Trading by sea has been a principal activity of all civilisations. However, moving goods and cargoes by water involves facing difficulties and dangers such as storms and bad weather, avoiding reefs, **headlands**, sandbanks and cliffs, and making safe passage into ports and harbours.

The earliest aids to navigation were beacons or **daymarks**, sited near harbours or ports rather than on headlands or reefs, to help ships reach their destinations safely. The earliest lighthouses were in the Mediterranean, and the oldest such structure of which written records survive was that on the island of Pharos, off Alexandria, on the northern coast of Egypt.

The Pharos lighthouse, which stood 142 metres (466 ft) tall, was built around 283 BC and stood until 1326.

Coal and lighthouses

The development of lighthouses around the coasts of the British Isles reflected **trade routes**. The earliest British lights were built on the south and east coasts to assist vessels trading with European ports. But by the 17th century, lights along the east coast helped to guide **colliers** carrying coal from the ports of the north-east to London.

The coal trade from Newcastle and Sunderland to London dominated coastal traffic. Just less than 50% of coastal shipping in the period 1779 to 1884 was devoted to coal carriage. Indeed, the coal trade was the largest single activity of coastal shipping during the industrial revolution.

Roker Pier Lighthouse, Sunderland
Built: 1903
Tower: 75 ft
Colour: red and white naturally coloured stone
Material: natural stone and granite
Builder: Henry Hay Wake

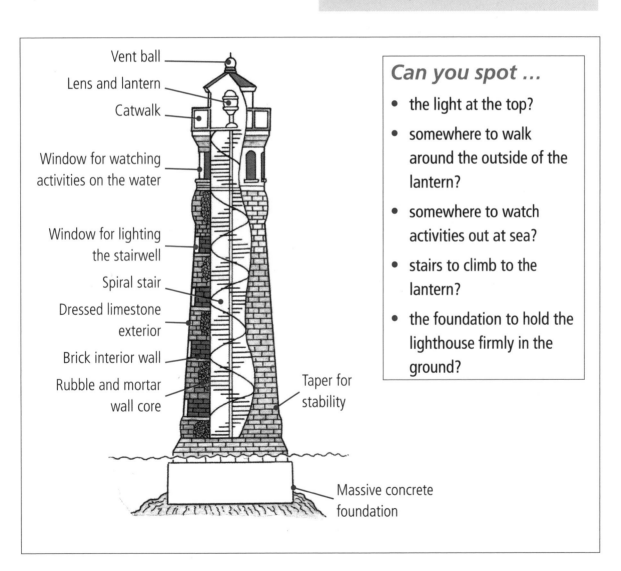

Vent ball
Lens and lantern
Catwalk
Window for watching activities on the water
Window for lighting the stairwell
Spiral stair
Dressed limestone exterior
Brick interior wall
Rubble and mortar wall core
Taper for stability
Massive concrete foundation

Can you spot ...

- the light at the top?
- somewhere to walk around the outside of the lantern?
- somewhere to watch activities out at sea?
- stairs to climb to the lantern?
- the foundation to hold the lighthouse firmly in the ground?

Author interview: *The Lighthouse Keeper's Lunch*

Ronda Armitage is the author of a very famous children's book series about a lighthouse keeper called Mr Grinling.

Where do you get your ideas from?

The idea for *The Lighthouse Keeper's Lunch* came from a question our son asked many years ago. My husband David and I had taken our children down to look at a lighthouse near us. We were standing on the cliffs when my son noticed a wire running from the cliff down to the lighthouse.

'What's that wire for?' he asked.

It was probably a wire taking electricity down to the lighthouse so the light would shine brightly out to sea every night, but David didn't say that.

'I expect that's for the lighthouse keeper's lunch,' David said.

DAVID TOLD A LIE!! Well, it was a sort of a lie but you could also say he was making up a story. Now that day I was wearing my best listening ears. I'm sure you've got some too. I was listening for stories.

'What a good idea,' I thought. 'That's what I could write a story about: a lighthouse keeper who gets his lunch in a basket down a wire.'

Victorian fact

A very famous story tells of a young, Victorian lighthouse keeper's daughter, called Grace Darling, who was born in 1815 in Bamburgh, Northumberland.

She is famous for helping her father, William Darling, in the rescue of survivors from the shipwrecked *Forfarshire* in 1838. Grace spotted the shipwreck of the *Forfarshire* from the windows of their home, in Longstone lighthouse, and is famous for participating in the rescue of survivors. She died aged only 26.

Glossary

- **headland** a narrow piece of land that projects from a coastline into the sea
- **daymark** a tall structure on land, only visible by day, which aids navigation by sailors
- **trade route** any route taken by ships carrying goods
- **collier** ship carrying coal

| Name: | Class: | Date: | Total marks: | /50 |

1 According to the text, why were lighthouses built?

Give **two** reasons from the text.

1. _____

2. _____

2 marks

2 Look at the section headed: *The first lights*.

What difficulties are faced when moving goods and cargoes by water?

Give **three** difficulties.

1. _____

2. _____

3. _____

3 marks

3 Why were beacons or daymarks sited near harbours or ports?

_____

_____

1 mark

/ 6

Total for this page

4 Look at the section headed: *Coal and lighthouses*.

Find and **copy two** facts about coal.

1. _____

2. _____

5 *The coal trade from Newcastle and Sunderland to London dominated coastal traffic.*

What does the word *dominated* mean in this sentence?

_____

_____

6 Look at the paragraph beginning: *The coal trade from Newcastle and Sunderland ...*

How do we know that the coal trade was the biggest activity?

_____

_____

/ 4

Total for this page

7 How tall is the Roker Pier Lighthouse?

_____

1 mark

8 What is the purpose of the **_Can you spot ..._** text box?

1 mark

Tick **two**.

to keep the reader engaged with the text ☐

to provide extra information ☐

to encourage the reader to look for technical information ☐

to show how the lighthouse works ☐

9 Look at the section headed: **_Where do you get your ideas from?_**
Explain how David's lie inspired Ronda Armitage to write her book.

1 mark

_____

_____

/3

Total for this page

10 Look at the section headed: **_Victorian fact_**.

Write a suitable heading to replace _Victorian fact_.

_____

1 mark

11 Why is Grace Darling famous?

_____

_____

1 mark

12 Match each event to the date it happened.

2 marks

Event		Date
The Pharos lighthouse was built.		1815
Grace Darling was born.		1838
The Forfarshire was shipwrecked.		1903
Roker Pier lighthouse was built.		283 BC

/ 4

Total for this page

Answers

Test 1

The story of the Minotaur

Qu.	Content domain	Answer & marking guidance	Mark
1	2a	petrifying	1
2	2d	**Award 1 mark** each for any **two** of the following: He was uncaring; cruel; selfish; wanted to look after his own people above others; scared of the Minotaur; a bully.	2
3	2b	the Minotaur	1
4	2c	Cannot allow the sacrifice to continue. / So it is the last time young citizens will be eaten. / To break the ritual of sending young citizens. / Because he wants to try to defeat the Minotaur.	1
5	2g	He was cruel.	1
6	2f	**Award 2 marks** for a developed response to the changing of the sails and the meaning of this. The paragraph is about the king asking Theseus to change the sails to white to show he was safe. The final paragraph is about Theseus forgetting to change the sails to white. **Award 1 mark** for a response to the changing of the sails.	2
7	2b	To put white sails on the ship.	1
8	2b	**Award 1 mark** for either of the following answers, or for both. She loved him. She thought her father would kill her because she helped Theseus.	1
9	2d	**Award 1 mark** each for any **two** of the following: She decided to help Theseus. / She gave Theseus a ball of string to help him. / She asked Theseus to take her back to Athens with him. / She described her father as cruel: *'To think that I am free of my cruel father …'.*	2
10	2d	Answer related either to continuing to pursue Theseus or to getting her revenge. She waited for a boat to pass and sailed to Theseus to beg him to marry her as she was still in love with him. / She took the next boat home to tell her father what had happened. Her father waged war against the Athenians.	1
11	2b	horror	1
12	2d	**Award 2 marks** for a point and explanation from the text. Aegeus felt heartbroken because he had tried to persuade Theseus not to go in the first place/had warned him of the dangers. / Aegeus was heartbroken because he thought his beloved son had been killed/he knew it was a dangerous thing to do. **Award 1 mark** for an undeveloped point. He was devastated/heartbroken.	2
13	2c	**Award 1 mark** for all **four** correct answers: At the centre of the maze was the Minotaur. *2* Theseus is picked up by the Minotaur. *3* King Minos builds a giant maze. *1 (given)* Aegeus presumes that Theseus has died. *5* Theseus and Ariadne sail across the calm seas. *4*	1

Things that go bump in the night!

Qu.	Content domain	Answer & marking guidance	Mark
14	2c	Do you think ghosts exist?	1
15	2b	**Award 1 mark** for finding both examples: 1. children 2. adults	1
16	2a	notion	1
17	2b	**Award 1 mark** for *According to tradition, ghosts are invisible but can permit humans to see them.*	1
18	2c 2b	a) haunted. b) **Award 1 mark** for either of the following: 　A monk haunts the rear terrace. 　King Edward VII's secretary died there and haunts it.	1 1
19	2a	residences **Do not accept** other words.	1
20	2b	Elizabeth I	1
21	2d/2a	**Award 1 mark** for answers that refer to his desire to leave the room, e.g. He really wanted to/had a desire to leave the room.	1
22	2a	**Award 1 mark** for *apparently*. Also accept *conjecture*. Only accept **one** word.	1
23	2b	John Brown	1
24	2b	**Award 2 marks** for all **five** correct and **1 mark** for **four** out of five correct answers. George III　　　room beneath the library (given) a monk　　　　　rear terrace Henry VIII　　　cloisters John Brown　　　corridors Elizabeth I　　　library	2
25	2d	**Award 3 marks** for a fully developed, text-based explanation for both positive and negative outcomes. Positive outcomes: money, e.g. tourism brings in money which means palaces can be conserved; improvements can be made to the palaces. Access to the real royal artefacts/sources, e.g. people can see what real palaces look like. Negative outcomes: congestion, e.g. car parks and roads get really busy; money, e.g. entrance prices cost a lot; damage to historic sources, e.g. objects are broken, taken; carpets and floors worn; environment, e.g. grounds get ruined; litter is spread. **Award 2 marks** for a fully developed, text-based explanation of either a positive or a negative outcome. **Award 1 mark** for two undeveloped points.	3
26	2f	**Award 1 mark** for all **four** correct answers. Do you believe in ghosts?　　introduces the debate about whether or not ghosts exist What is a ghost?　　　　　　gives information about the description of a ghost Ghosts at royal residences　　highlights the different ghosts that lived in palaces and castles Royal ghosts – at what cost? presents the differing viewpoints on having ghosts	1

The lion and Albert

Qu.	Content domain	Answer & marking guidance	Mark
27	2a	famous	1
28	2b	**Award 1 mark** for correctly finding and copying a line which includes dialect words, e.g. *'E'd a stick with an 'orse's 'ead 'andle.*	1
29	2c	The family were bored by the seaside so they went to the zoo.	1
30	2b	**Award 1 mark** for **two** animals. lions / tigers / camels	1
31	2d	He didn't think it was right that he should be lying so peacefully. / He thought lions were supposed to be ferocious, so he wanted to do something to make him act like this.	1
32	2g	To show that he didn't have much fear. / To show he wasn't one tiny bit scared.	1
33	2b	He poked his stick in the lion's ear.	1
34	2d	**Award 3 marks for two acceptable points, at least one with evidence.** He is brave/fearless because he knew the lion was ferocious and wild but he still approached it. He is naughty/badly behaved because he pushed the stick into the lion's/Wallace's ear even though he was lying peacefully. **Award 2 marks for either two acceptable points, or one acceptable point with evidence.** He is brave/fearless and naughty. **Award 1 mark for one acceptable point.** He is brave.	3
35	2d	**Award 1 mark** for stating that he is wearing his best clothes. Also accept a quote from the text: *All dressed in his best.*	1
36	2d	**Award 2 marks** for one feeling with evidence from the text. Mother is angry/annoyed/cross because the lion had eaten Albert and she had paid to come in. Other reasons: because she had turned a bit awkward and felt that someone had to be summoned / because she says that she is not wasting all of her life to have children and then feed them to the lions. **Award 1 mark** for one acceptable point. Mother is angry/annoyed/cross.	2
37	2d	life is unpredictable.	1
38	2f	to entertain	1
39	2h	Accept a comparison between initial worry/vex from Mother and then the feeling of not too bothered. At first she is *vexed* or worried. Then she says she is not having any more children to feed lions. At the end of the poem, she does not seem too bothered about Albert.	1

Test 2

Lighthouse history

Qu.	Content domain	Answer & marking guidance	Mark
1	2b	**Award 2 marks** for two correct reasons given in the text. To mark major headlands and sandbanks. To offer light at entrances to ports, harbours and rivers.	2
2	2b	**Award 1 mark** for each correct answer. Up to a maximum of **3 marks**. storms / bad weather / avoiding reefs, headlands, sandbanks, cliffs / making safe passage into ports and harbours	3
3	2b	**Award 1 mark** for answers that suggest that it was to help ships reach their destinations safely.	1
4	2b	**Award 1 mark** each for any **two** of the following: By the 17th century, lights along the east coast helped to guide colliers carrying coal from the ports of the north-east to London. The coal trade from Newcastle and Sunderland to London dominated coastal traffic. Just less than 50% of shipping in the period 1779 to 1884 was devoted to coal carriage. The coal trade was the largest single activity of coastal shipping during the industrial revolution.	2
5	2a	took over/led/ruled/made up the greatest part of	1
6	2b	**Award 1 mark** for answers that refer to it being the single biggest activity, e.g. it says that it was the largest single activity of coastal shipping during the industrial revolution.	1
7	2b	75 ft	1
8	2f	**Award 1 mark** for **both** of the following: to keep the reader engaged with the text to provide extra information	1
9	2d	Children may or may not quote. Answers must refer to the link between David's lie to his son and the idea for a book/story where a lighthouse keeper gets his lunch on a wire.	1
10	2c	**Award 1 mark** for answers related to her name and/or the role of Grace Darling: The story of Grace Darling / Grace Darling and the shipwreck of *Forfarshire* / Grace Darling rescues survivors of shipwreck / The role of Grace Darling / Survivors of shipwreck rescued	1
11	2b	**Award 1 mark** for correctly stating that Grace Darling is famous for helping her father rescue survivors from the shipwrecked *Forfarshire*.	1
12	2b	**Award 2 marks** for all four correct answers and **1 mark** for two or three correct answers. The Pharos lighthouse was built. 283 BC Grace Darling was born. 1815 The *Forfarshire* was shipwrecked. 1838 Roker Pier lighthouse was built. 1903	2
13	2b	**Award 1 mark** for two correct answers and **2 marks** for all three correct: |	True	False
---	---	---
The Pharos lighthouse was 200 metres tall.		✔
Almost 100% of coastal shipping in the period 1779 to 1884 was devoted to coal carriage.		✔
The lighthouse was tapered for stability.	✔ (given)	
Grace Darling died aged 26.	✔			2
14	2f	to inform	1

The hollow land

Qu.	Content domain	Answer & marking guidance	Mark
15	2d	**Award up to 2 marks:** **1 mark** related to the shape created by the miners. **1 mark** for references to the absence left by the miners. The miners have gone so all that is left is the hollow, created when they were digging out coal.	2
16	2d	**Award 1 mark** for any **two** of the following: They will mow all day and through the night. It takes all members of the family to help. They didn't finish the High Field until tea-time and then they began the Home Field. By ten or eleven o'clock at night they are still working.	2
17	2d	**Award 1 mark** for **two** answers: They can afford to buy packaged food, so they must be wealthy. They can afford to keep dogs as pets rather than as working animals.	1
18	2g	It spreads across the hillside.	1
19	2a	racket	1
20	2b	**Award 1 mark** for **three** correct or **2 marks** for all **four** correct: <table><tr><td></td><td>True</td><td>False</td></tr><tr><td>The hollow land used to have miners working there.</td><td>✔</td><td></td></tr><tr><td>There are lots of farming families living in the hollow land.</td><td></td><td>✔</td></tr><tr><td>There are wild horses in Wateryate Bottom.</td><td>✔</td><td></td></tr><tr><td>A big family live in Bell Teesdale's gran and grandad's old house.</td><td>✔</td><td></td></tr></table>	2
21	2b	**Award 1 mark** each for any **two** of the following: The racket they make can be heard as far as Garsdale. / They have music playing, lads yelling and laughing and a radio or two going. / Their telephone rings.	2
22	2h	**Award 1 mark** each for any **two** of the following: They are from the city. / They buy, rent or lease the little houses. / They have big estate cars, not a tractor. / They eat packet food. / They're noisy. / The mother cooks Italian-style food. / They have a fridge and a telephone. / The Batemans' dog is a pet whereas the Teesdales' dogs are working dogs. / The Batemans play loud music and listen to the radio.	2
23	2b	**Award 1 mark** for answers that refer to them being out all night doing the hay/at hay-time.	1
24	2g	**Award 1 mark** for it's really noisy/loud or a similar description.	1
25	2d	the London family	1
26	2e	**Award 2 marks** for an explanation related to Mr Bateman being cross with the noise and with reference to the text. For example, Mr Bateman might come out and shout at the Teesdales for making noise because now it is 11 o'clock and they want to go to bed/the tractor is making a racket. **Award 1 mark** for a simple explanation with no reference to the text. He might come out and shout. / He might be cross at the noise.	2

The Lady of Shalott

Qu.	Content domain	Answer & marking guidance	Mark
27	2d	**Award 1 mark** for reference to the fact that the countryside is completely covered by fields of barley and rye. / It is completely covered in long fields of barley and of rye.	1
28	2g	It is suitable because the water is chilly so the daffodils are shaking/shivering with the cold. / So you can imagine the daffodils shaking with cold as they stand next to the chilly water.	1
29	2g	The Lady of Shalott's voice is so beautiful that it sounds out of this world/sent from heaven.	1
30	2b	They can hear her chanting and singing.	1
31	2b	**Award 1 mark** for **two** different answers. She lives in a tower. / She wears a pearl garland around her head. / She sleeps on a velvet bed. / She is dressed in royal clothing (*apparelled*).	1
32	2b	She has to weave night and day.	1
33	2b	*To weave the mirror's magic sights*	1
34	2d	**Award 3 marks** for **two** acceptable points (impressions), at least one with evidence. She is bored because she has no time for sport and play. She is unhappy/has little joy because she has to weave all day and has a curse on her. She is unhappy because she says she is *half sick of shadows*. **Award 2 marks** for either **two** acceptable points, or **one** acceptable point with evidence. She is unhappy and bored. **Award 1 mark** for **one** acceptable point. She is unhappy.	3
35	2d	Her weaving/threads.	1
36	2c	**Award 1 mark** for **two** answers: is inside a tower. is under a curse.	1

Test 3

Crystals

Qu.	Content domain	Answer & marking guidance	Mark
1	2b	**Award 2 marks** for all **three** correct answers and **1 mark** for **two** correct answers. perfection/transparency/clarity	2
2	2b	ice	1
3	2c	Where can crystals be found?	1
4	2b	**Award 1 mark** each for any **two** of the following: freezer, fridge, washing machine, TV, telephone, radio, camera, bikes, cars	2
5	2b	**Award 1 mark** for each correct answer. Maximum **2 marks**. Used in control circuits/machines/communications/medicine/diamond blades/scalpels for surgery.	2
6	2h	**Award 1 mark** each for any **two** of the following: They do not corrode; others do. / They are the hardest crystal. / They can be used in surgery. / Other crystals are not used in surgery. **Do not accept** 'Diamonds are colourless'.	2
7	2b	F. Mohs	1

Qu.	Content domain	Answer & marking guidance	Mark
8	2b	**Award 1 mark** for **all four** correctly ordered: diamond *1* (given) topaz *2* apatite *3* fluorite *4* gypsum *5*	1
9	2a	shine	1
10	2b	To cut and polish stones. / To turn stones into objects of beauty.	1
11	2c	**Award 2 marks** for all **five** correct and **1 mark** for **four** out of five correct answers. Did you know? explains what a material is (given) Crystals at home highlights how everyday objects are crystalline Fact gives information about how diamonds do not corrode Hardness gives information about how hard particular minerals are Making them sparkle! explains how rough crystals can be transformed	2
12	2d	**Award 2 marks** for all four correct and **1 mark** for **three** correct answers. |	Fact	Opinion
---	---	---
We live in a crystal planet.	✔	
Water is made from hydrogen and oxygen.	✔	
A crystal's colour can be its most striking feature.		✔
Some crystals are beautifully shaped.		✔		2

Macavity, the mystery cat

Qu.	Content domain	Answer & marking guidance	Mark
13	2g	**Award 1 mark** for an explanation of the word *master* and **1 mark** for an explanation of the word *criminal*. For example, the word *criminal* suggests that Macavity is breaking the law deliberately and the word *master* suggests that he is very good at it.	2
14	2a	bafflement	1
15	2d	**Award 2 marks** for a developed response that recognises he is clever. For example: Macavity is an intelligent cat so he doesn't leave any evidence of what he's done. **Award 1 mark** for a simple response. For example: He is too clever to be caught.	2
16	2d	That he is very agile and can climb walls/buildings, etc. very easily.	1
17	2b	**Award 1 mark** for each correct answer. Maximum of **2 marks**. His coat is dusty from neglect. / His whiskers are uncombed. / He doesn't wash.	2
18	2b	a snake	1
19	2g	**Award 1 mark** for answers that refer to Macavity as being a monster/evil/villain dressed up like a cat. For example: It suggests that Macavity is evil.	1
20	2b	'It must *have been Macavity!'*	1
21	2b 2d	**Award 1 mark** for each correct answer. Maximum of **2 marks.** He does things that are impossible for a cat to do: breaks the law of gravity/cheats at cards/steals jewels/steals plans/does long division sums.	2
22	2a	clever and thoughtful	1

The travels of Marianne North

Qu.	Content domain	Answer & marking guidance	Mark
23	2b	Because women rarely travelled alone.	1
24	2a	favourite thing/love/passion/hobby/obsession	1
25	2b	She wanted to paint (the intriguing) Monkey Puzzle trees.	1
26	2d	**Award 2 marks** for developed responses with reference to the text. For example: She includes details of many flowers and plants she has seen or painted. The flower names often use scientific words for plants such as Roystonea regia. She knows about science to know all these names. **Award 1 mark** for simple response with reference to the text. She knows the other/real names of many flowers like Roystonea regia. She knows the names of many flowers like Roystonea regia.	2
27	2g	She wrote many long diary entries. / She kept a diary for a long time/many years.	1
28	2b	royal palms	1
29	2g	**Award 1 mark** for answers referring to the rough texture of the flower. For example, it tells you that the flower was rough or prickly which gives you an image of what it looked like.	1
30	2d	**Award 1 mark** for answers that refer to the fact that she used local forms of transport that ordinary people would use. **Award 1 mark** for an example from the text. For example: She used local/normal forms of transport, such as riding on the back of a mule/ travelling in a jampany/riding in a mule-drawn cart/travelling on a steamship/riding on horseback/riding in a train/being carried in a jinricksha and a palki.	2
31	2d	**Award 3 marks** for **two** acceptable points, at least **one** with evidence. She still travelled because she enjoyed travelling and knew that there would be lots of adventures. She wanted to discover different plants because it says that, *my first work was to attempt to make a sketch of the great avenue of royal palms.* **Award 2 marks** for either **two** acceptable points, or **one** acceptable point with evidence. She enjoyed travelling and she wanted to discover different plants. **Award 1 mark** for **one** acceptable point. She enjoyed travelling.	3
32	2c	was a Victorian artist.	1
33	2d	**Award 3 marks** for **two** acceptable points, at least **one** with evidence. Award marks for answers that refer to what she does even though she has to overcome certain hurdles. For example: She was determined because she supported women even though some of them *irritated* her and *made stupid remarks*. She was also determined because even though she was ill, she still travelled to Chile to *paint the intriguing Monkey Puzzle trees.* **Award 2 marks** for either **two** acceptable points, or **one** acceptable point with evidence. For example: She supported women and she painted Monkey Puzzle trees even though she was ill. **Award 1 mark** for **one** acceptable point. She supported women.	3
34	2b	Award **1 mark** for all **four** correct answers. |	True	False
---	---	---
Marianne North's mother and father died at the same time.		✔
Marianne reached Lisbon on 13th August at sunrise.		✔
In South Africa Marianne saw stamens dancing.	✔	
Marianne North retired to a house in Gloucestershire.	✔			1

13 Using the information from the text, put a tick in the correct box to show whether each statement is **true** or **false**.

One has been done for you.

	True	False
The Pharos lighthouse was 200 metres tall.		
Almost 100% of coastal shipping in the period 1779 to 1884 was devoted to coal carriage.		
The lighthouse was tapered for stability.	✔	
Grace Darling died aged 26.		

2 marks

14 What is the purpose of this text?

Tick **one**.

to entertain ☐

to persuade ☐

to inform ☐

to recount ☐

1 mark

/3

Total for this page

The hollow land

I'm Bell Teesdale. I'm a lad. I'm eight.

All down this dale where I live there's dozens of little houses with grass growing between the stones and for years there's been none of them wanted. They're too old or too far out or that bit too high for farmers now. There was miners once – it's what's called the hollow land – but they're here no more. So the little houses is all **forsook**. They have big **garths** round them, and pasture for grass-letting – sheep and that – and grand hay fields. Maybe just too many buttercups blowing silver in June, but grand hay for all that, given a fair week or two after dipping time.

All these little farm houses for years stood empty, all the old farming families gone and the roofs falling in and the swallows and swifts swooping into bedrooms and muck trailing down inside the stone walls. So incomers come. They buy these little houses when they can, or they rent or lease them. Manchester folks or even London folks, with big estate cars full of packet food you don't see round here, and great soft dogs that's never seen another animal.

All down Mallerstang there's **becks** running down off the **fell**. It's **bonny**. Down off the sharp **scales**, dry in summer till one single drop of rain sends them running and rushing and tumbling down the fell-side like threads of silk. Like cob-webs. And when the wind blow across the dale these becks gasp, and they rise up on themselves like the wild horses in Wateryate Bottom. They rise up on their hind legs. Or like smoke blowing, like ever so many bonfires, not water at all, all smoking in the wind between Castledale and the Moorcock toward Wensleydale. It's bonny.

And townsfolk come looking at all this now where once they only went to the Lake District over the west. Renting and leasing they come. Talking south. 'Why'd they come?' I ask our grandad who's leased the farm house he used to live in (my gran died). 'There's not owt for 'em here. What's use of a farm to them? Just for sitting in. Never a thing going on.'

'Resting,' says my grandad. 'They take 'em for resting in after London.'

Well, this family that come to my grandad's old house, Light Trees, wasn't resting. Not resting at all. There's a mother and a father and four or five great lads, some of them friends only, and there's a little lad, Harry, and the racket they make can be heard as far as Garsdale likely.

They has the house – our gran and grandad's old house see – but we still keep all the farm buildings and work them and we've right to the hay off the Home Field.

There's good cow **byres**, dipping pens, **bull's hull** and clipping shed. So we're clipping and dipping and drenching and putting the cows to the bull regardless. Sometimes there's a hundred sheep solid across our yard so they can't get their car over to the yard gate. But it was in the arrangement, mind. My dad always says, 'We're about to bring in sheep, Mr Bateman' – it's what they're called, Bateman – 'We're bringing in sheep. Would you like to get your car out first? We'll hold things back.' There's maybe four, five and six of our sheep-dogs lying watching, and their soft dog lying watching our dogs, but never going near.

Then from out the house comes their music playing, and lads yelling and laughing and a radio or two going and the London mother cooking these Italian-style suppers and their telephone ringing (they've got in the telephone like they've got in a fridge) and they're all saying, this London lot, '*Beautiful* evening Mr Teesdale' – my dad – 'And what are you doing with the sheep tonight? You're giving us quite an *education*.'

And there's this little lad, Harry, just stands there not saying owt.

Now there's one night, the first night of hay-time, and we're all **slathered out**, even my dad. It's perfect. A right hot summer and a right hot night and a bright moon. Yesterday my dad said, 'Tomorrow we'll mow hay. We'll mow all day and if need be through the night. There may be rain by Sunday.'

He's never wrong, my dad, so we – my mum and our Eileen and our Eileen's boyfriend and Grandad and all of us – we set up and we finish the High Field and Miner's Acre by tea-time. And then we sets to with the Home Field – that's the great big good field round Light Trees. Light Trees stand right in it.

It makes a rare clatter our tractor and cutter, louder than their **transistors** – clatter, clatter, clatter, round and round and round – and after a bit, well maybe two hours, their heads beginning to bob from windows. Then round ten-eleven o'clock and the summer light starts fading and it's still clatter, clatter, there's electric lights flashing on and off inside Light Trees and this London father comes out.

Glossary

- **forsook** abandoned
- **garths** large open spaces
- **becks** streams
- **fell** mountain
- **bonny** pretty
- **scales** slopes
- **byres** cowsheds
- **bull's hull** outbuilding for holding bulls
- **slathered out** exhausted
- **transistors** radios

15 Look at the paragraph beginning: *All down this dale where I live ...*

Why do you think this area of land in the Dales is known as *the hollow land*?

_____

_____

16 The text suggests that the fields that need mowing are very large.

Give **two** details to support this idea.

1. _____

2. _____

2 marks

17 Look at the paragraph beginning: *All these little farm houses ...*

What **two differences** does the text suggest about people from Manchester and London, and people from the Dales?

1 mark

1. _____

2. _____

/5

Total for this page

18 *... dry in summer till one single drop of rain sends them running and rushing and tumbling down the fell-side like threads of silk. Like cob-webs.*

What does the description above suggest about the stream?

1 mark

Tick **one**.

It is very dry. ☐

It spreads across the hillside. ☐

It is a spiderweb. ☐

It is burning and smoking. ☐

19 Look at the paragraph beginning: *Well, this family that come ...*

Find and **copy one** word that is closest in meaning to *making a loud noise.*

1 mark

_____

20 Using the information from page 33, put a tick in the correct box to show whether each statement is **true** or **false**.

2 marks

	True	False
The hollow land used to have miners working there.		
There are lots of farming families living in the hollow land.		
There are wild horses in Wateryate Bottom.		
A big family live in Bell Teesdale's gran and grandad's old house.		

21 The Bateman family is noisy.

Give **two** details to support this.

2 marks

1. _____

2. _____

22 Give **two** details to show how the Batemans are different to the Teesdales.

2 marks

1. _____

2. _____

/ 6

Total for this page

23 Look at the paragraph beginning: *Now there's one night, …*

Why were the Teesdale family exhausted?

_____

1 mark

24 Look at the paragraph beginning: *It makes a rare clatter our tractor … clatter, clatter, clatter*

What does the description above tell you about the tractor?

_____

1 mark

25 *… their heads beginning to bob from windows.*

Who is this description about?

_____

1 mark

26 Look at the last sentence of the final paragraph.

What might the London father do when he comes out of the house?

Explain fully, using evidence from the text to support your answer.

_____

_____

_____

2 marks

/ 5

Total for this page

The Lady of Shalott

Part I

On either side the river lie
Long fields of barley and of rye,
That clothe the **wold** and meet the sky;
And thro' the field the road runs by
    To many-tower'd Camelot;
The yellow-leaved waterlily
The green-sheathed daffodilly
Tremble in the water chilly
    Round about Shalott.

Willows whiten, aspens shiver.
The sunbeam showers break and quiver
In the stream that runneth ever
By the island in the river
    Flowing down to Camelot.
Four grey walls, and four grey towers
Overlook a space of flowers,
And the silent isle **imbowers**
    The Lady of Shalott.

Underneath the bearded barley,
The **reaper**, reaping late and early,
Hears her ever chanting cheerly,
Like an angel, singing clearly,
    O'er the stream of Camelot.
Piling the sheaves in furrows airy,
Beneath the moon, the reaper weary
Listening whispers, 'Tis the fairy,
    Lady of Shalott.'

The little isle is all **inrail'd**
With a rose-fence, and **overtrail'd**
With roses: by the marge **unhail'd**
The **shallop** flitteth silken sail'd,
    Skimming down to Camelot.
A pearl garland winds her head:
She leaneth on a velvet bed,
Full royally **apparelled**,
    The Lady of Shalott.

Glossary

- **wold** countryside
- **imbowers** shelters
- **reaper** farmer
- **inrail'd** enclosed
- **overtrail'd** overgrown
- **unhail'd** unnoticed
- **shallop** boat
- **apparelled** clothed

Part II

No time hath she to sport and play:
A charmed web she weaves away.
A curse is on her, if she stay
Her weaving, either night or day,
    To look down to Camelot.
She knows not what the curse may be;
Therefore she weaveth steadily,
Therefore no other care hath she,
    The Lady of Shalott.

She lives with little joy or fear.
Over the water, running near,
The sheepbell tinkles in her ear.
Before her hangs a mirror clear,
     Reflecting tower'd Camelot.
And as the mazy web she whirls,
She sees the surly village **churls**,
And the red cloaks of market girls
    Pass onward from Shalott.

Sometimes a troop of damsels glad,
An abbot on an ambling **pad**,
Sometimes a curly shepherd lad,
Or long-hair'd page in crimson clad,
    Goes by to tower'd Camelot:
And sometimes thro' the mirror blue
The knights come riding two and two:
She hath no loyal knight and true,
    The Lady of Shalott.

But in her web she still delights
To weave the mirror's magic sights,
For often thro' the silent nights
A funeral, with plumes and lights
    And music, came from Camelot:
Or when the moon was overhead
Came two young lovers lately wed;
'I am half sick of shadows,' said
    The Lady of Shalott.

Glossary

- **churls** villagers
- **pad** road

27 Look at the first verse.

Long fields of barley and of rye,

That clothe the wold [countryside] *and meet the sky; ...*

What does this description tell you about the countryside?

_____

_____

1 mark

28 *The green-sheathed daffodilly*

Tremble in the water chilly

Why is *tremble* a suitable word to describe the daffodils?

_____

_____

1 mark

29 *Like an angel, singing clearly ...*

What impression do you get from this description of the Lady of Shalott?

_____

_____

1 mark

/3

Total for this page

30 How do the people of Camelot know the lady is in the tower?

_____

_____

1 mark

31 Look at Part I.

How can you tell that the Lady of Shalott is royal?

Give **two** different ways.

1. _____

2. _____

1 mark

32 Look at Part II: _A curse is on her, if she stay …_

What curse has been placed on this lady?

_____

_____

1 mark

33 The lady weaves the things she sees in her mirror.

Find and **copy one** quote to support this idea.

_____

1 mark

/ 4

Total for this page

34 What impression do you get of the Lady of Shalott's feelings?

Give **two** impressions, using evidence from the text to support your answer.

3 marks

Impression	Evidence
_____	_____ _____ _____
_____	_____ _____ _____

35 Look at Part II: *But in her web she still delights …*

What is her web?

1 mark

_____

36 The main ideas of the poem are that the Lady of Shalott …

                    Tick **two**.

1 mark

is inside a tower.   ☐

is looking at a tower.   ☐

lives in Camelot.   ☐

is under a curse.   ☐

/5

Total for this page

Test 3

Crystals

Crystals are associated with perfection, transparency and clarity. Many crystals fit these ideals, especially those cut as gemstones, but most are neither perfect nor transparent. Crystals are solid materials in which the atoms are arranged in a regular pattern.

Did you know?

A material can exist as a solid, a liquid or a gas depending on its temperature.

Water is made of atoms of hydrogen and oxygen bound together to form molecules. In its solid form (ice), the water molecules are arranged in a regular order and form a crystalline solid.

A world of crystals

Crystals are all around us. We live on a crystal planet in a crystal world. The rocks which form the Earth, the Moon and meteorites (pieces of rock from space), are made up of minerals and virtually all of these minerals are made up of crystals. Crystalline particles make up mountains and form the ocean floors. When we cross the beach we tread on crystals.

Crystals at home and at work

We use crystals at home and at work; indeed, crystals are vital to today's technology.

Crystals at home

Many everyday objects in the home are crystalline. There are ice crystals in the freezer, salt and sugar crystals in the food cupboard and in food itself. There are silicon crystal chips in the fridge and washing machine. The TV, telephone, radio and camera work because of crystals. The house is built of materials which are mostly crystalline, and outside, bikes and cars stand slowly rusting – crystallising!

Crystals at work

Crystals are used in control circuits, machines, communications and medicine.

> ### Fact
>
> Diamonds do not corrode. This is one reason why sometimes diamond blades are used in scalpels for surgery.

The colour of crystals

The colour of a crystal can be its most striking feature. The causes of colour are varied and many minerals occur in a range of colours.

For example, quartz, diamond, beryl and corundum can be red, green, yellow and blue.

What is it?

This is the first question to ask about a mineral, crystal or gemstone. Most minerals have a clearly identifiable crystal structure. Colour and surface features can be studied using a hand lens. Other properties, such as 'hardness', can be studied using scientific equipment.

Hardness

The property of hardness is dependent upon the strength of the forces holding atoms together in a solid.

The scale below was devised by F. Mohs in 1812.

Mineral	Talc	Gypsum	Calcite	Fluorite	Apatite
Hardness	1	2	3	4	5

Mineral	Orthoclase	Quartz	Topaz	Corundum	Diamond
Hardness	6	7	8	9	10

Making them sparkle!

Some rough crystals are beautifully shaped and have breathtaking lustre and colour, but most are worn down or have other imperfections. A skilled stone cutter and polisher, called a 'lapidary', can turn these stones into objects of beauty and value by using their individual qualities in the right way.

| Name: | Class: | Date: | Total marks: | /50 |

1 Look at the first section.

What are crystals associated with?

Give **three** things.

1. _____

2. _____

3. _____

2 marks

2 Look at the section headed: *Did you know?*

What is water in its solid state?

_____

1 mark

3 Look at the section headed: *A world of crystals*.

Which of the following would be a suitable replacement for this sub-heading?

Tick **one**.

What are crystal pieces called? ☐

What can crystals do? ☐

Where can crystals be found? ☐

Why are crystals found on beaches? ☐

1 mark

/ 4

Total for this page

4 Give **two** household machines that contain crystals, according to the text.

2 marks

1. _____

2. _____

5 How are crystals used in the workplace?

Give **two** uses.

2 marks

1. _____

2. _____

6 Give **two** ways to explain how diamonds are different compared to other crystals.

2 marks

1. _____

2. _____

/ 6

Total for this page

7 Look at the section headed: *Hardness*.

Who developed the scale used to measure the hardness of crystals?

_____

1 mark

8 Number these crystals 1–5 in order of hardness.

Number 1, the hardest crystal, has been done for you.

1 mark

fluorite ☐

topaz ☐

apatite ☐

gypsum ☐

diamond ☐ 1

9 *Some rough crystals are beautifully shaped and have breathtaking lustre …*

What does the word *lustre* mean in this sentence?

1 mark

Tick **one**.

colour ☐

shape ☐

shine ☐

cut ☐

/3

Total for this page

10 What is the job of a lapidary?

_____

_____

1 mark

11 Draw lines to match each section to its main content.

One has been done for you.

2 marks

Section	Content
Did you know?	explains how rough crystals can be transformed
Crystals at home	gives information about how hard particular minerals are
Fact	highlights how everyday objects are crystalline
Hardness	explains what a material is
Making them sparkle!	gives information about how diamonds do not corrode

12 Using information from the text, tick one box in each row to show whether each statement is a **fact** or an **opinion**.

2 marks

	Fact	Opinion
We live on a crystal planet.		
Water is made from hydrogen and oxygen.		
A crystal's colour can be its most striking feature.		
Some crystals are beautifully shaped.		

/5

Total for this page

51

Macavity, the mystery cat

Macavity's a Mystery Cat: he's called the Hidden Paw –

For he's the master criminal who can defy the Law.

He's the bafflement of Scotland Yard, the Flying Squad's despair:

For when they reach the scene of crime – *Macavity's not there!*

Macavity, Macavity, there's no one like Macavity,

He's broken every human law, he breaks the law of gravity.

His powers of levitation would make a **fakir** stare,

And when you reach the scene of crime – *Macavity's not there!*

You may seek him in the basement, you may look up in the air –

But I tell you once and once again, *Macavity's not there!*

Macavity's a ginger cat, he's very tall and thin;

You would know him if you saw him, for his eyes are sunken in.

His brow is deeply lined with thought, his head is highly domed;

His coat is dusty from neglect, his whiskers are uncombed.

He sways his head from side to side, with movements like a snake;

And when you think he's half asleep, he's always wide awake.

Macavity, Macavity, there's no one like Macavity,

For he's a fiend in feline shape, a monster of depravity.

You may meet him in a by-street, you may see him in the square –

But when a crime's discovered, then *Macavity's not there!*

He's outwardly respectable. (They say he cheats at cards.)

And his footprints are not found in any file of Scotland Yard's.

And when the larder's looted, or the jewel-case is rifled,

Or when the milk is missing, or another Peke's been stifled,

Or the greenhouse glass is broken, and the trellis past repair –

Ay, there's the wonder of the thing! *Macavity's not there!*

And when the Foreign Office find a Treaty's gone astray,

Or the Admiralty lose some plans and drawings by the way,

There may be a scrap of paper in the hall or on the stair –

But it's useless to investigate – *Macavity's not there!*

And when the loss has been disclosed, the Secret Service say:

'It *must* have been Macavity!' – but he's a mile away.

You'll be sure to find him resting, or a-licking of his thumbs,

Or engaged in doing complicated long division sums.

Glossary

- **fakir** a Muslim or Hindu holy man who appeared to have magic powers

13 Look at the first paragraph.

Macavity is described as the *master criminal.*

What does this description suggest about Macavity?

Explain **both** words.

_____

_____

2 marks

14 Look at the first paragraph.

Find and **copy one** word that means the same as *confusion.*

_____

1 mark

15 Why do you think Macavity never gets caught?

_____

_____

_____

2 marks

16 *His powers of levitation would make a fakir stare, ...*

What does this sentence tell you about Macavity's physical abilities?

_____

_____

1 mark

/6

*Total for
this page*

17 Macavity is not very clean.

Give **two different** pieces of evidence from the text to support this.

1. _____

2. _____

2 marks

18 What does the text compare the way Macavity moves his head to?

Tick **one**.

a chicken ☐

a snake ☐

a goat ☐

an elephant ☐

1 mark

19 Look at the fourth verse.

... a fiend in a feline shape ...

What does the word *fiend* suggest about Macavity?

_____

1 mark

/ 4

Total for this page

55

20 Look at the sixth verse.

Find and **copy** a group of words that shows the Secret Service knows who is responsible for the missing things.

_____

1 mark

21 In what ways is Macavity's behaviour extraordinary?

Give **two** ways.

1. _____

2. _____

2 marks

22 According to what you have read, which description best matches the character of Macavity?

1 mark

Tick **one**.

brave and friendly ☐

magical and vain ☐

violent and shy ☐

clever and thoughtful ☐

/ 4

Total for this page

The travels of Marianne North

Marianne North was an accomplished painter, knowledgeable botanist, enthusiastic traveller and prolific diarist.

She was a remarkable Victorian artist who travelled around the world to satisfy her passion for painting plants. At a time when women rarely travelled alone, many of Marianne's expeditions to remote areas of the globe were fraught with danger, but also with adventure and opportunity.

The life of Marianne North

Marianne North was born in Hastings, Sussex, in 1830. She spent much of her youth travelling in England and Europe, and although she took a sketchbook, as was customary for young Victorian women travellers, music was her mania.

Algerian stamp showing Marianne North

When Marianne was 24, her mother died and when her father died in 1869, Marianne was at last free to visit the tropics. She once wrote that she was 'a very wild bird' and liked 'liberty'. At the age of 40 she began her astonishing series of trips around the world.

Between 1871 and 1885, she visited 16 different countries. Her aim was to paint plants in their habitats and to educate people on the sources of certain products.

Marianne North was a prolific diarist, recording many descriptive and creative accounts of her travels. Read some of her adventures on the next page.

Did you know?

Royal connections Marianne received some tuition from a famous Dutch flower artist and from Valentine Bartholomew, flower painter to Queen Victoria.

Brazil 1872

I started in the *Neva* Royal Mail ship on August 9, 1872. I had a most comfortable cabin, quite a little room, with a square window, and the voyage was most enjoyable. Lisbon was our first halt, which we reached on August 13 at sunset; the entrance to the harbour is striking, with the semi-**Moorish** tower and convent of Bela in the foreground.

Brazil 1872–1883

Of course my first work was to attempt to make a sketch of the great avenue of royal palms (Roystonea regia), which has been so often described.

There was a coarse marigold-looking bloom with the sweetest scent of vanilla, and a large purple-bell begonia creeper with the strongest smell of garlic. A lovely velvet-leaved ipomoea, with large white blossom and dark eye, and a perfectly exquisite rose-coloured begonia bush were very common.

South Africa 1882–1883

While painting the protea flower, I saw the stamens begin to dance, and out came a big green beetle.

Did you know?

Marianne North travelled on many different means of transport which included:

Riding on the back of a mule, travelling in a **jampany**, riding in a mule-drawn cart, travelling on a steamship, riding on horseback, riding in a train, being carried in a **jinricksha** and a **palki**!

Marianne North Gallery at Kew Gardens

Marianne North's paintings can be seen in the Marianne North Gallery at the Royal Botanic Gardens, Kew, designed by her friend James Fergusson. The gallery includes coloured oil paintings of plants, landscapes, birds and animals and includes over 800 paintings.

Did you know?

Marianne North completed over 800 paintings in less than 14 years!

Women artists

Marianne was a great supporter of women. She was particularly keen to promote the work of other women artists (although she was often irritated by certain young ladies who made stupid remarks about her paintings).

In 1884, at the end of her trip to the Seychelles, Marianne's health began to break down. She returned to England, but after a brief rest she decided to visit Chile. She was determined to paint the intriguing Monkey Puzzle trees she knew she would find there. After a stop in Jamaica, she returned from this, her final voyage, in 1885.

Marianne continued arranging the paintings in her gallery and finally retired to a house in Gloucestershire where she made a wonderful garden. Marianne North died on August 30, 1890 at the age of only 59.

Fact

Marianne North met Charles Darwin who told her to 'investigate the flora of Australia and New Zealand'. She took this as a 'royal command' and went at once.

Glossary

- **Moorish** built by the Moors, people from North Africa who invaded Spain
- **jampany** a kind of armchair, with a pole on each side, carried by four men
- **jinricksha** Japanese word for rickshaw, a small, two-wheeled, cart-like passenger vehicle with a fold-down top, pulled by one person
- **palki** a Sikh word for a small, raised platform with canopy for a very important person

23 Look at the first paragraph.

Why were many of Marianne's travels *fraught with danger*?

_____

1 mark

24 *... although she took a sketchbook, as was customary for young Victorian women travellers, music was her mania.*

What does the word *mania* mean in this sentence?

_____

1 mark

25 Why was Marianne determined to go to Chile?

_____

1 mark

/ 3

Total for this page

26 Marianne North *could* have been a botanist (someone who studies the science of plants) as well as a painter.

Explain why this could be a possibility, using evidence from the text.

_____

_____

2 marks

27 Marianne North was a *prolific diarist.*

What does the word *prolific* tell you about Marianne North as a diarist?

_____

_____

1 mark

28 Look at the section headed: ***Brazil 1872–1883***.

What are *Roystonea regia*?

_____

1 mark

/4

Total for this page   **61**

29 Look at the section headed: ***Brazil 1872–1883***.

... coarse marigold-looking bloom ...

What does the word *coarse* tell you about the flower?

_____

_____

1 mark

30 What do the types of transport Marianne used tell you about the ways in which she travelled?

Give an example from the text to support your answer.

_____

_____

2 marks

/3

*Total for
this page*

31 Why did Marianne travel around the world when she knew there would be areas that were *fraught with danger*?

Explain **two** reasons, using evidence from the text to support your answer.

1. _____

_____

_____

2. _____

_____

_____

3 marks

32 The main idea in this text is that Marianne North …

Tick **one**.

was a Victorian woman.	☐
painted thousands of exotic plants.	☐
has a gallery at Kew Gardens.	☐
was a Victorian artist.	☐

1 mark

/ 4

Total for this page 63

33 Look at the section headed: *Women artists*.

Marianne North has a very determined character.

Explain **two** ways she is determined, using evidence from the text to support your answer.

1. _____

_____

_____

2. _____

_____

_____

34 Using the whole text, put a tick in the correct box to show whether each statement is **true** or **false**.

	True	False
Marianne North's mother and father died at the same time.		
Marianne reached Lisbon on 13th August at sunrise.		
In South Africa Marianne saw stamens dancing.		
Marianne North retired to a house in Gloucestershire.		

/ 4

Total for this page